AMAZING ANIMAL TALES

Baby Koala

The feathertail glider stretches
out its folds of skin to glide
between trees. Can you spot
one on every page?

AMAZING ANIMAL TALES

ANNE ROONEY QU LAN

OXFORD
UNIVERSITY PRESS

Dust drifts through the trees under a scorching sun. High in a tree, a koala sleeps peacefully in the cool shade of the leaves.

Hidden inside a cosy pouch on Mum's tummy, Baby Koala rests, too. The tree sways in the wind, rocking Baby Koala back to sleep when she stirs.

Koalas sleep in a crook of the branches.
With a tough but furry bottom, it's not too uncomfy!

Can you spot five
sleepy koalas?

Koalas live in the Australian bush where they eat eucalyptus (gum tree) leaves.

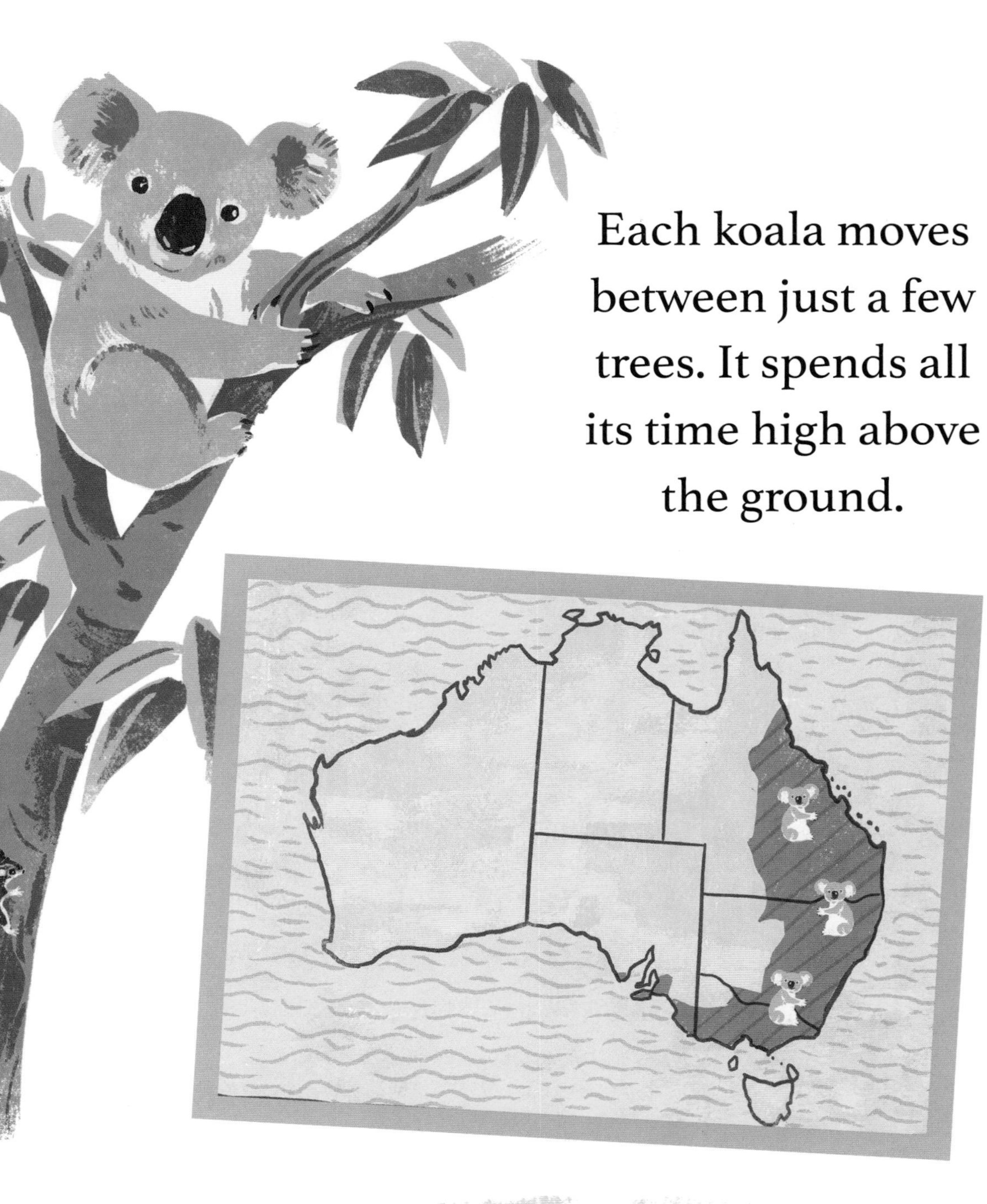

Each koala moves between just a few trees. It spends all its time high above the ground.

Baby Koala grows bigger every day. After a few months, a furry head peeps from the pouch.

Brightly-coloured birds flit and dart between the leaves. Their chattering and screeching is too loud for Baby Koala's new ears. She creeps back into the calm of Mum's pouch.

As the spring flowers bloom, it's a tight squeeze in the pouch. Baby Koala clings to Mum's thick fur for their journeys through the treetops.

Baby Koala is getting bigger and bolder. She bravely creeps from Mum's back and curls her fingers around rough bark.

Carefully,

carefully,

she climbs.

What are these leaves like?

Tough — but **tasty!**

A newborn koala baby weighs as little as ten honeybees.

The baby is the size of a jellybean, about 2 centimetres long. Measure your finger against this newborn koala.

20 19 18 17 16 15 14 13 12 11 10 9 8 7 6 5 4 3 2 1 0

A baby koala is called a joey. It is born blind and deaf, without fur. For six months, it grows in its mother's pouch, sucking milk.

A million glittering stars sparkle above the night-time forest.

What's this? It looks like a dry leaf, but —

Oh!

The moth flutters up in a flurry of powdery wings. Baby Koala bats it away, and wobbles on the branch. She grips extra tightly — she mustn't fall!

Suddenly, a shape looms from the darkness. It swoops on silent wings, hooked claws ready to grab —

What? ME?

Baby Koala hurries to Mum and
wriggles her fingers into soothing fur.
The owl must find another dinner tonight.

The joey has teeth from nine months and can start to eat eucalyptus leaves.

Eucalyptus leaves are poisonous to most animals, but the poison doesn't hurt koalas.

It still has milk, too, until it's a year old.

Muscles keep the pouch shut so that the baby koala doesn't fall out. The joey is safe in its mum's pouch.

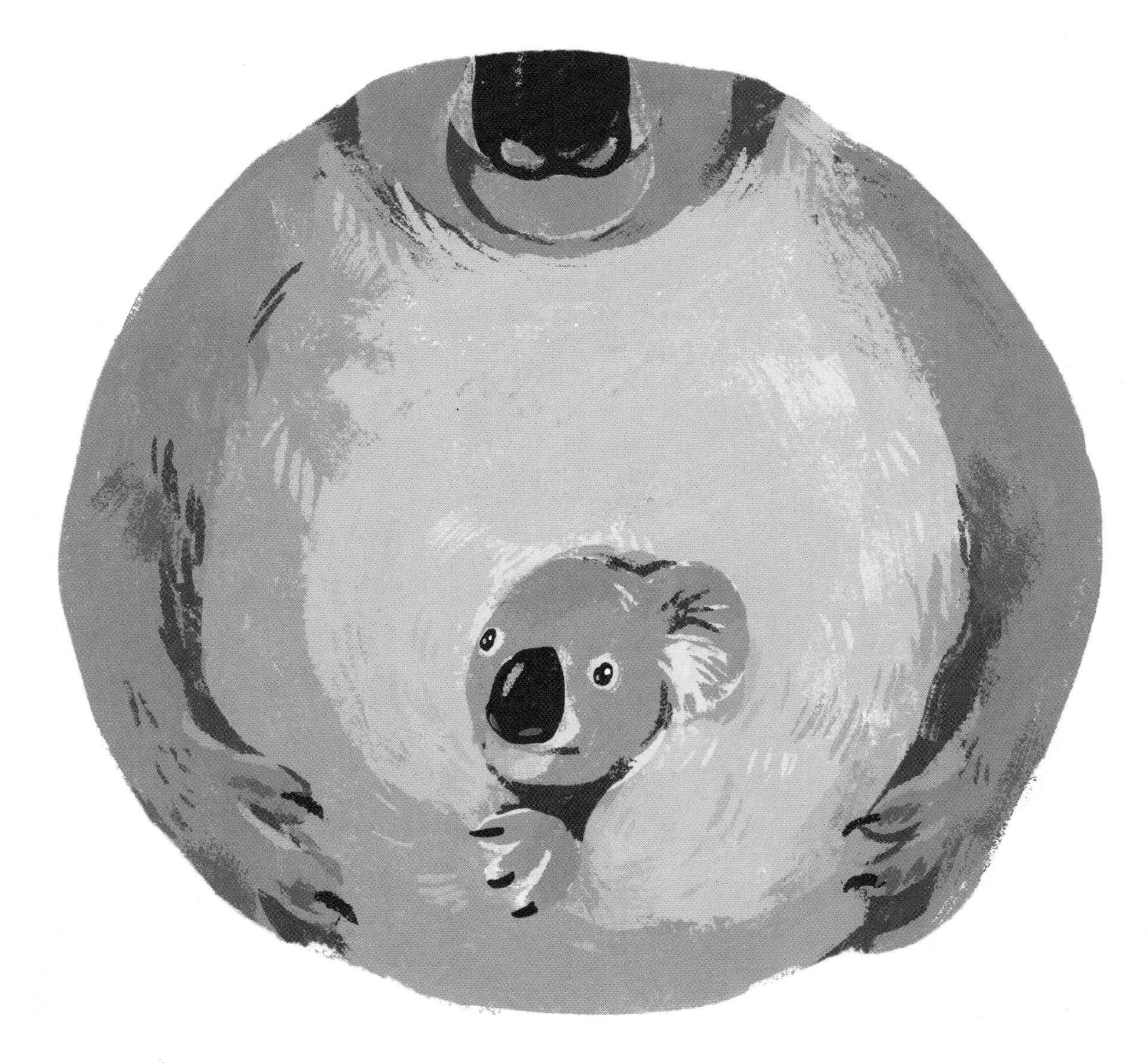

It peeps out when it's five or six months old.

Today is hotter than ever and tumbling grey clouds block the scorching sun. The air tastes wrong. Mum sniffs it and shuffles away along the branch.

Baby Koala clings to Mum as black specks swirl and sting her eyes. A frightened possum skitters up their tree.

What's happening?

Suddenly, the sky flares red. Birds and animals shriek as the forest crackles and roars below.

Mum clambers further up the tree and Baby Koala hurries behind, her paws slipping on the bark and her heart racing. She longs for Mum to carry her, but she can't quite catch up!

Wait for me!

Flames leap
from tree to tree.
At last, Baby Koala
grips Mum's fur and
scrambles onto her back.

Soon the wind changes and the smoke blows the other way.
Baby Koala watches, calmer now the danger is over.
The fire passes, the flames far away again.

As the smoke drifts away, the animals come safely back to their homes.

Safe at last, Baby Koala snuggles into Mum's fur and snuffles drowsily. The sun slants over the forest, warming the sky as she drifts into sleep.

Goodnight, Baby Koala!

Koalas have fingerprints, just like you.

Can you see the lines
on your fingertips?

After 9-10 months, the joey is too big for the pouch.

It clings to its mother's back as she clambers and even leaps through trees to feed.

OXFORD
UNIVERSITY PRESS

Great Clarendon Street, Oxford OX2 6DP
Oxford University Press is a department of the University of Oxford.
It furthers the University's objective of excellence in research, scholarship,
and education by publishing worldwide. Oxford is a registered trade mark
of Oxford University Press in the UK and in certain other countries

First published in 2022

British Library Cataloguing in Publication Data
Data available

ISBN: 978-0-19-278087-4

1 3 5 7 9 10 8 6 4 2

Printed in China

Paper used in the production of this book is a natural,
recyclable product made from wood grown in sustainable forests.
The manufacturing process conforms to the environmental
regulations of the country of origin.